PORTALS TO READING

Reading Skills Through Literature

FANTASTIC MR. FOX

Roald Dahl

Reproducible Activity Boc

The *Portals to Reading* series accompanies time-tested literature that should be an important part of every school's reading program. The activities will reinforce a wide variety of language and reading skills which are generally part of the curriculum at the reading level of the novel. However, the *Portals* pick-and-choose format gives you the final decision about which activities will enhance your students' personal learning.

The activities in this book are based on sentences and paragraphs especially written to support the teaching objective of each lesson. Clearly, such literary matters as style and flavor may be experienced only by reading the book itself. Thus, the words of the author have been left where they belong—in their pure form in the pages of the novel.

Table of Contents

Word Attack Skills

Comprehension Skills

Study Skills

Creative Skills

Author! Author!
ROALD DAHL

Born in South Wales in 1916, Roald Dahl was the son of a shipbroker, painter, and horticulturist who left his family of seven children a modest fortune when he died in 1920.

Dahl was educated at a boarding school, which he remembers for the "horrors, fierce discipline, no talking in the dormitories, no running in the corridors, no untidiness of any sort, no this or that or the other, just rules, rules and still more rules that had to be obeyed."

Dahl served in the Royal Air Force during World War II and was shot down over Egypt. After recuperating from this experience, he was sent to Washington and interviewed. He wrote his own story based on this experience and had it published in *The Saturday Evening Post.*

In 1943, Dahl wrote his first children's story. He continued to write for adults, as well, drawing on his war experiences.

In 1953, he married actress Patricia Neal. The couple had four children. One daughter died of measles encephalitis when she was seven. A son suffered from hydrocephalus brought on by an accident.

Patricia, too, had her share of serious health problems. Her story was televised as "The Patricia Neal Story" in 1981. This movie told of Patricia's return to health following a stroke which affected her speech and ability to use her arms and legs.

Dahl is widely known for his adult and children's literature, short stories, and screenplays. He is probably best known for his much-loved tale, *Charlie and the Chocolate Factory.*

The Story in Brief

Mr. Fox *must* be fantastic to stand up to three angry farmers and save his weasel, rabbit, mole, and badger friends.

The fox versus farmers war begins when Mr. Fox raids the Boggis, Bunce, and Bean farms to bring food home for his hungry family. Once and for all, the farmers decide they're going to outfox that devious Mr. Fox. They try digging up the Fox family's hole. Then they resort to shovels and tractors and attempts to starve the wily creatures.

But Mr. Fox outwits the three angry farmers every time. In fact, he manages to dig tunnels to each of the three farms so that his family and friends can help themselves to the farmers' food for the rest of their lives. And that, of course, makes him pretty fantastic in the eyes of his family and friends.

Using Short Vowels

Read the words in the word box. Each word contains a short vowel sound. Say the words to yourself and listen for the short vowel sounds. Then read each sentence. Choose a word from the word box to complete each sentence.

cleverest	shotgun	~~chicken~~
smothered	robber	gallons
pot-bellied	nasty	stuffed
disgusting	temper	

Example: Boggis was a _____*chicken*_____ farmer.

1. Farmer Boggis ate three boiled chickens _____ with dumplings for every meal.

2. Farmer Bunce was a _____ dwarf.

3. Mashed goose livers made a _____ paste.

4. Bunce _____ the liver paste into doughnuts.

5. Bunce had a bad _____ because of the food he ate.

6. Farmer Bean was the _____ of all three farmers.

7. Bean drank _____ of strong apple cider.

8. The farmer hid with his _____, hoping to catch the fox.

9. Each night the farmers waited for the _____.

10. Boggis, Bunce, and Bean were _____ men.

FANTASTIC MR. FOX

Using Long Vowels

Read the words in the word box. Each word contains a long vowel sound. Say the words to yourself and listen for the long vowel sounds. Then read each sentence. Choose a word from the word box to complete each sentence.

beastly	approached	huge
change	nose	paste
~~owners~~	night	hoping
creep	cider	

Example: Boggis, Bunce, and Bean were the _____*owners*_____ of three farms in the valley.

1. Bunce stuffed doughnuts with goose liver _____.

2. Bunce's diet gave him a _____ temper.

3. Bean used the apples in his orchard to make strong _____.

4. Mr. and Mrs. Fox lived in a hole under a _____ tree.

5. Every evening, Mr. Fox would _____ down into the valley to steal food.

6. Every _____ the three farmers hid in a dark place.

7. Boggis, Bunce, and Bean were _____ to catch the fox.

8. Mr. Fox _____ the farms with the wind blowing in his face.

9. Mr. Fox would _____ direction if he smelled Boggis.

10. Mr. Fox had a fantastic _____.

FANTASTIC MR. FOX

Using Compound Words

The word box contains all compound words. Compounds are made by putting two smaller words together. Read each compound word. Then read the sentences below. In the blank in each sentence, write the compound that best completes the sentence.

some/one	out/side
sweet/heart	flash/light
every/one	no/body
~~some/where~~	down/ward
near/by	blood/stained
moon/light	

Example: The moon was shining _____*somewhere*_____.

1. The farmers waited _____ the entrance to the foxes' hole.

2. Mr. Fox heard what sounded like _____ moving through the dry leaves.

3. Mr. Fox caught the glint of something bright behind a _____ tree.

4. He saw a spot of _____ shining on a polished surface.

5. One of the farmers shone a _____ on the hole.

6. Outside the hole lay the _____ remains of Mr. Fox's tail.

7. Mrs. Fox called her husband _____ and licked the stump of his tail to stop the bleeding.

8. "_____ can dig faster than a fox," shouted Mr. Fox.

9. _____ in the Fox family worked together to dig the tunnel.

10. The foxes tunneled _____ from the hole.

FANTASTIC MR. FOX

Listening for Syllables

Say each of the words below to yourself. The number of vowel sounds you hear in each word will be the same as the number of syllables. Decide how many syllables are in each word. Then write the number on the blank line after each word.

Example: children ___2___

1. poisonous	_____	16. listened	_____
2. entrance	_____	17. awake	_____
3. opposite	_____	18. quivering	_____
4. direction	_____	19. whispered	_____
5. polished	_____	20. gathered	_____
6. especially	_____	21. suddenly	_____
7. inched	_____	22. jumped	_____
8. twitched	_____	23. shouted	_____
9. flattened	_____	24. furiously	_____
10. tattered	_____	25. gradually	_____
11. missed	_____	26. together	_____
12. foxes	_____	27. stopped	_____
13. dozed	_____	28. tunnel	_____
14. suppose	_____	29. breath	_____
15. possible	_____	30. fantastic	_____

Finding Base Words

Each word below has been made by adding an ending such as *-ly*, *-ed*, or *-ing* to a base word. On the blank beside each word, write the base word.

Example: careful _____*care*_____

1. filthy _____

2. poisonous _____

3. gases _____

4. chosen _____

5. poked _____

6. sniffing _____

7. gently _____

8. tossing _____

9. shovels _____

10. tenderly _____

11. finest _____

12. foxes _____

13. sharply _____

14. scraping _____

15. quicker _____

16. digging _____

17. beginning _____

18. furiously _____

19. possibly _____

20. loved _____

FANTASTIC MR. FOX

Remembering Details

The following questions are about some of the characters and events in the book. Write the answers on the lines below the questions. Be sure to use complete sentences.

1. Why did Bean have trouble hearing what Bunce and Boggis were saying?

   _____

2. What was Bean's new idea for digging Mr. Fox out of his hole?_____

   _____

3. What machines did the farmers get? _____

   _____

4. What did Mrs. Fox think was happening when she heard the mechanical

   shovels digging? _____

5. How would the foxes know when they were gaining ground?_____

   _____

6. Why didn't the farmers stop digging and eat lunch? _____

   _____

7. How did the farmers feel when the crowds of people jeered and laughed at

   them? _____

   _____

Classifying Words

In each group of words below, one word does not belong with the others. Read all four words in each group. Decide which word doesn't belong and cross it out.

Example: Boggis   Bunce   ~~Mr. Fox~~   Bean

1. ground   boil   soil   earth

2. monsters   tractors   machines   mechanical shovels

3. clanking   banging   clanging   cursing

4. minutes   beginning   hour   day

5. hilltop   crater   hole   tunnel

6. called   shouted   stared   yelled

7. afternoon   listening   lunchtime   evening

8. panted   walked   trotted   waddled

9. jeered   laughed   smiled   declared

10. cross   tired   furious   mad

Determining Cause and Effect

To determine a cause, ask "What is the reason?"
To determine an effect, ask "What is the result?"
Match the causes and effects below. Write the
number of the cause in front of its effect.

Cause	**Effect**
1. Bunce and Bean were tired from driving.	_____ Bean's face was purple with rage.
2. Bean was furious that they hadn't caught the fox.	_____ Everyone saw Bean's scarlet gums and teeth.
3. The three farmers made an oath.	_____ The three farmers shook hands.
4. Bunce asked what they should do next.	_____ Bunce and Bean stopped the tractors and climbed down.
5. Bean showed a sickly smile.	_____ Bean said Bunce should go down the hole after the fox.

1. The farmers decided to camp outside Mr. Fox's hole.	_____ Men were sent to watch the other side of the hill.
2. Boggis held a steaming chicken near the foxes' hole.	_____ The foxes could smell the hot chicken.
3. Soon darkness fell.	_____ Mr. Fox could smell Bean.
4. Boggis was worried the fox would dig through to the other side of the hill.	_____ Mr. Fox would be unable to come out for food.
5. Bean smelled bad because he never bathed.	_____ Bunce and Bean switched on the tractors' headlamps.

Chapters 7-8

Matching Synonyms

A synonym is a word having the same or nearly the same meaning as another word. Read each sentence. Choose a synonym from the word box to replace the italicized word.

covered	sure	get
sincere	red	anger
cooked	floated	smell
~~turned~~	squatting	

Example: _____*turned*_____ Bean *switched* off the motor of his tractor and climbed down.

_____ 1. Bean was filled with *rage* because they hadn't been able to dig out the foxes.

_____ 2. The three farmers swore a *solemn* oath that they wouldn't give up.

_____ 3. Bean thought Bunce should go down the hole to *fetch* Mr. Fox.

_____ 4. When Bean smiled, more of his *scarlet* gums showed than his teeth.

_____ 5. Boggis held a *steaming* chicken over the foxes' hole.

_____ 6. The foxes were tempted by the rich *scent* of chicken.

_____ 7. The foxes were *crouching* at the bottom of their tunnel.

_____ 8. Boggis ate three chickens *smothered* in dumplings.

_____ 9. The foxes felt hungrier as the smell of food *wafted* down the tunnel to them.

_____ 10. Mr. Fox was *positive* the three farmers were still waiting outside his hole.

FANTASTIC MR. FOX

Classifying Word Groups

Read the following sentences. Decide if the italicized part of the sentence tells you *where*, *when*, or *how*. Underline the correct choice.

Example: *Down in the tunnel*, the foxes were
starving to death.   <u>where</u>   when   how

1. Mrs. Fox said she'd rather die *in peace* than
face the farmers' guns.   where   when   how

2. Mr. Fox was sitting *quite still*.   where   when   how

3. Mr. Fox glanced back *at his wife*.   where   when   how

4. Mr. Fox's excitement could be seen *in his eyes*.   where   when   how

5. Mrs. Fox spoke *quickly*.   where   when   how

6. The foxes were hungry *after three days and
nights* without food.   where   when   how

7. Mrs. Fox *slowly* got to her feet.   where   when   how

8. "We can handle this *by ourselves*," said Mr. Fox.   where   when   how

9. Mr. Fox told the children the tunnel would go
in a very special direction.   where   when   how

(continued)

Name _____

10. They kept digging and *little by little* the tunnel grew.   where   when   how

11. There were no days or nights *in the murky tunnel.*   where   when   how

12. *At last,* Mr. Fox gave the order to stop.   where   when   how

13. The foxes began to slope the tunnel *up towards the surface.*   where   when   how

14. The foxes ended up *right underneath somebody's house.*   where   when   how

15. *Then* Mr. Fox chose three of the plumpest hens.   where   when   how

FANTASTIC MR. FOX

Remembering Details

The following questions are about some of the characters and events in the book. Write the answers on the lines below the questions. Be sure to use complete sentences.

1. What did Mrs. Fox say when one of the Small Foxes wanted to dash out of the hole for food and water? _____

_____

2. Why didn't Mr. Fox think his idea would work? _____

_____

3. Which of the foxes was too weak to dig? _____

_____

4. Why wouldn't Mr. Fox tell the Small Foxes where they were going as they dug their tunnel? _____

_____

5. Why didn't the foxes know how long they had been digging? _____

_____

6. Where did the foxes' tunnel take them? _____

_____

7. Why was Mr. Fox careful to replace the floorboards when they left the chicken house? _____

_____

FANTASTIC MR. FOX

Discovering Meaning Through Context

Read the following sentences. Three meanings are given for each italicized word. Use the context of the sentence to figure out which meaning is correct. Underline the correct meaning.

Example: The Small Foxes would have been happy to have a tiny *sip* of water.

<u>drink</u>   pitcher   pool

1. One of the Small Foxes wanted to sneak out of the hole and make a *dash* for it before the farmers noticed.

   pinch   run   hyphen

2. Mrs. Fox was weak and *suffering* more than the others.

   hurting   crying   sleeping

3. Mr. Fox told the children that they were headed for a *marvelous* place that would make them very excited.

   quiet   huge   wonderful

4. It was hard to see in the *murky* tunnel.

   deep   cold   dim

(continued)

**Discovering Meaning
Through Context**

Chapters 9-10

5. Mr. Fox told the others it was time to take a *peep* upstairs to see where
they were.

      chicken   look   trip

6. The foxes began to *slope* the tunnel up towards the surface.

      leave   slant   close

7. Mr. Fox pushed up a board and poked his head through the *gap*.

      opening   tunnel   door

8. Mr. Fox was so excited he let out a *shriek*.

      jump   scream   secret

9. The whole shed was *teeming* with thousands of chickens.

      clucking   playing   filled

10. "Take these chickens to your mother and tell her to *prepare* a feast for us
all," said Mr. Fox.

      make   eat   enjoy

FANTASTIC MR. FOX

Using Cloze Reading

Read the paragraphs below. Use the words in the word box to fill in the blanks. The first example is done for you.

Mummy	weaker	food
fantastic	strength	~~tunnel~~
dreaming	House	bursting
three	feast	

Small Fox hurried back along the (1) _____*tunnel*_____ . He was

happily carrying the (2) _____ plump hens. He came

(3) _____ in upon Mrs. Fox. "Look, (4) _____!"

he cried.

Mrs. Fox opened one eye. By now, she was (5) _____ than

ever. "I must be (6) _____," she thought as she saw the

chickens.

Small Fox explained how they had tunnelled through to Boggis' Chicken

(7) _____ Number One. This news and the sight of the

(8) _____ gave Mrs. Fox new (9) _____. She

began to prepare a (10) _____ for the family to enjoy when

Mr. Fox returned. "Your father is truly a (11) _____ fox!" said

Mrs. Fox.

Matching Synonyms

A synonym is a word having the same or nearly the same meaning as another word. Read each sentence. Choose a synonym from the word box to replace the italicized word.

part	~~confusion~~	closest
promise	angrily	fat
tell	left	ran
dug	all	

Example: _____confusion_____ Badger explained about the *chaos* up on the hill.

_____ 1. The foxes had *tunnelled* right up through the floor.

_____ 2. Mr. Fox explained the next *bit* of his plan.

_____ 3. There were three Small Foxes *remaining* to help dig.

_____ 4. Weasel could sneak out of the *tightest* spots.

_____ 5. "It's all your fault," said Badger *furiously*.

_____ 6. Mr. Fox told Badger about the feast of *plump*, juicy chickens.

_____ 7. Mr. Fox knew the mess was *entirely* his fault.

_____ 8. "I can *assure* you there'll be enough food for all," said Mr. Fox.

_____ 9. Small Badger *scrambled* quickly back through the hole in the roof.

_____ 10. Badger's small son ran back to *spread* the news.

Chapter 13

Matching Antonyms

An antonym is a word that means the opposite or nearly the opposite of another word. Read each sentence. Choose an antonym from the word box to replace the italicized word.

tasteless	bored	dull
borrowing	above	worst
untrained	~~thin~~	noise
hate	tough	

Example: _____*thin*_____ Mr. Fox chose four *plump*, young ducks.

_____ 1. Badger and Mr. Fox dug on in *silence*.

_____ 2. The digging went much faster with Badger *lending* a paw.

_____ 3. The two diggers crouched *underneath* another wooden floor.

_____ 4. Mr. Fox grinned and showed his *sharp*, white teeth.

_____ 5. The Small Foxes felt even hungrier thinking of the juicy, *tender* ducks.

_____ 6. The animals were *overwhelmed* by the sight of all the food.

_____ 7. Bunce's Mighty Storehouse had the *finest* and fattest ducks and geese.

_____ 8. Mr. Fox studied the food with an *expert* eye.

_____ 9. Badger jumped forward to grab the *luscious* food.

_____ 10. "I *adore* smoked ham," said Mr. Fox.

Determining Alphabetical Order

Words are listed in a dictionary in alphabetical order. Number the five words in each list below to show the order in which they would appear in the dictionary. Write a *1* in the blank before the word that comes first alphabetically, and so on.

Example:

_2_ digging

_5_ dug

_1_ digger

_3_ directly

_4_ ducks

A.

_____ geese

_____ grinned

_____ ground

_____ gap

_____ gaped

B.

_____ smoked

_____ suddenly

_____ sprang

_____ suspended

_____ snapped

C.

_____ morsels

_____ market

_____ mouths

_____ mad

_____ magnificent

D.

_____ carrots

_____ crouched

_____ close

_____ corner

_____ carts

E.

_____ worry

_____ world

_____ whole

_____ wrong

_____ wall

FANTASTIC MR. FOX

Choosing Correct Meanings

~~sharp~~	beat	turn
mind	sip	foot
close	head	

Each of the words in the word box can have more than one meaning. Read the sentences below. Complete each sentence by writing one of the words from the word box in the blank space. You will use each word twice.

Example: Mr. Fox was too _____*sharp*_____ to be fooled by Rat.

1. Rat told Mr. Fox to _____ his own business.

2. Badger took his _____ and sampled the cider.

3. Mr. Fox showed his _____, white teeth.

4. "_____ it!" yelled Rat when the other animals entered the cellar.

5. Rat wanted to _____ his cider in peace.

6. Mrs. Bean told Mabel she could stuff fox's _____ and hang it on the wall.

7. Mabel paused at the _____ of the steps.

8. Mr. Fox hardly breathed as Mabel got _____ to his hiding place.

9. Mrs. Bean changed her _____ about how much cider to bring upstairs.

(continued)

Choosing
Correct Meanings
Chapters 15-16

10. "Wow!" exclaimed Smallest Fox after he took a _____ of cider.

11. Mabel placed one _____ on the stairs and the animals scrambled to hide.

12. Now Mr. Fox was sure they could _____ the farmers.

13. Soon it was time to _____ back down the tunnel.

14. Mabel stopped to _____ the door.

15. Smallest Fox had to _____ around to see all of the jugs of cider.

FANTASTIC MR. FOX

Using Guide Words

At the top of each dictionary page are guide words. These words are the first and last words on a dictionary page. The other words on the page fall in alphabetical order between the guide words.

Put the words in the word box in alphabetical order under the correct guide words. The first one has been done for you.

~~brick~~	face	crept
Mabel	gloom	hundreds
glass	jar	cellar
noticed	morning	second
shelf	poison	fellow

act—fin	**final—march**	**mare—tongue**
1. _brick_	1. _____	1. _____
2. _____	2. _____	2. _____
3. _____	3. _____	3. _____
4. _____	4. _____	4. _____
5. _____	5. _____	5. _____

Writing a Journal Sample

Imagine that you are Smallest Fox. In the sample journal below, tell about the great feast.

FANTASTIC MR. FOX

Creating a Picture

Draw one of the scenes the author describes in chapter 17 or 18. Then write your own description of what you have drawn.

_____

_____

Recalling a Character

Think about a character from this book. Imagine that you are describing this character to someone who has not read the book. Write your description of the character. Try to include information about the character's appearance, likes and dislikes, behavior, friends, family, and so forth.

Character: _____

_____

_____

_____

_____

_____

_____

_____

_____

_____

_____

_____

Writing a Book Recommendation

Do you think other students would enjoy reading *Fantastic Mr. Fox?* On the lines below, explain why you would recommend reading the book. Mention specific things you liked about the story. For example, did you think the characters were funny? Did you like the way Mr. Fox tricked the farmers? If you didn't like the book, tell why you would not recommend it.

_____

_____

_____

_____

_____

_____

_____

_____

_____

_____

_____

Explaining Feelings

The questions below ask you to describe the feelings you had as you read the book. Read each question carefully. Write your response on the lines provided. Explain why you felt the way you did.

1. How did you feel when the farmers shot off Mr. Fox's tail?

_____

_____

_____

2. How did you feel when Bean and Bunce started using mechanical shovels?

_____

_____

_____

3. How did you feel when the people laughed and jeered at the three farmers?

_____

_____

_____

(continued)

Explaining Feelings

4. How did you feel when the farmers decided to camp out by the hole and wait for the foxes to starve to death?

_____

_____

_____

5. How did you feel when Mr. Fox found Boggis's Chicken House Number One?

_____

_____

_____

6. How did you feel when the animals enjoyed a big feast?

_____

_____

_____

7. How did you feel when the farmers were left waiting in vain for Mr. Fox?

_____

_____

_____

Optional Spelling and Vocabulary Lists

Below are four word lists from the book. The words can be used as spelling or vocabulary words.

Chapters 1-5

enormously	glum
shallow	frightening
doughnuts	electric
tummy-ache	scrunching
orchard	clogged
cleverest	machinery
rage	mechanical
lurking	murderous
delicately	mouthfuls
crafty	matchstick

Chapters 6-10

desperate	headlamps
clanking	hatchets
mighty	pistols
prowling	undefeated
dwarfish	disappointment
maniacs	whispered
extraordinary	floorboards
obstinate	cautiously
miserable	prancing
powerful	properly

Chapters 11-14

exploding	dangling
bursting	ravenously
murmured	saliva
strength	loot
plucking	trolley
foggiest	respectable
delicious	gentle
galore	decent
terrific	scraped
paradise	underground

Chapters 15-18

crumbly	business
saucy	clumsy
brilliant	brute
damp	quivering
accustomed	glorious
medicine	stretch
banquet	conversation
gurgled	colossal
sunbeams	trickling
inserted	famished

Supplementary Activities

Below is a list of ideas that could be used as supplementary or culminating activities.

I. Oral reading

    A. To the entire class

    B. To each other

    C. To the teacher

    D. To a tape recorder

II. Group discussions

    A. Author's writing style

    B. Ideas gained from the book

    C. Parts of the book

        1. Most important

        2. Most humorous

        3. Most saddening

        4. Most exciting

        5. Most liked

    D. Characters

        1. Did the characters seem real?

        2. What did you like best about each character?

        3. What did you dislike most about each character?

        4. Which character was the student's favorite? Why?

        5. List questions to ask each character.

(continued)

III. Spelling bee using words from the book

IV. Role play situations from the book

V. Artistic creations

    A. Murals

    B. Dioramas

    C. Book jackets

    D. Posters

    E. Puppets

    F. Poetry

    G. Costumes

    H. Portraits

    I. Mobiles

    J. Songs

    K. Newspaper headlines, articles, and drawings

VI. Research

    A. Foxes

    B. Apple orchards

    C. Badgers

    D. Rats

    E. Machines

    F. Farming

VII. Read other books by the same author

Response Key

WORD ATTACK SKILLS

Using Short Vowels (page 7)

1. smothered; 2. pot-bellied; 3. disgusting; 4. stuffed; 5. temper; 6. cleverest; 7. gallons; 8. shotgun; 9. robber; 10. nasty

Using Long Vowels (page 8)

1. paste; 2. beastly; 3. cider; 4. huge; 5. creep; 6. night; 7. hoping; 8. approached; 9. change; 10. nose

Using Compound Words (page 9)

1. outside; 2. someone; 3. nearby; 4. moonlight; 5. flashlight; 6. bloodstained; 7. sweetheart; 8. nobody; 9. everyone; 10. downward

Listening for Syllables (page 10)

1. 3; 2. 2; 3. 3; 4. 3; 5. 2; 6. 4; 7. 1; 8. 1; 9. 2; 10. 2; 11. 1; 12. 2; 13. 1; 14. 2; 15. 3; 16. 2; 17. 2; 18. 3; 19. 2; 20. 2; 21. 3; 22. 1; 23. 2; 24. 4; 25. 4; 26. 3; 27. 1; 28. 2; 29. 1; 30. 3

Finding Base Words (page 11)

1. filth; 2. poison; 3. gas; 4. chose; 5. poke; 6. sniff; 7. gentle; 8. toss; 9. shovel; 10. tender; 11. fine; 12. fox; 13. sharp; 14. scrape; 15. quick; 16. dig; 17. begin; 18. furious; 19. possible; 20. love

COMPREHENSION SKILLS

Remembering Details (page 12)

1. Bean's earholes were clogged because he never took a bath. 2. Bean suggested using machines. 3. The farmers got two enormous caterpillar tractors with mechanical shovels. 4. Mrs. Fox thought there was an earthquake. 5. The digging sounds made by the shovels would grow fainter. 6. They were too keen on catching the fox. 7. They were more determined than ever to catch the fox.

Classifying Words (page 13)

1. boil; 2. monsters; 3. cursing; 4. beginning; 5. hilltop; 6. stared; 7. listening; 8. panted; 9. declared; 10. tired

Determining Cause and Effect (page 14)

Set 1: 2; 5; 3; 1; 4
Set 2: 4; 2; 5; 1; 3

Matching Synonyms (page 15)

1. anger; 2. sincere; 3. get; 4. red; 5. cooked; 6. smell; 7. squatting; 8. covered; 9. floated; 10. sure

Classifying Word Groups (page 16)

1. how; 2. how; 3. where; 4. where; 5. how; 6. when; 7. how; 8. how; 9. where; 10. how; 11. where; 12. when; 13. where; 14. where; 15. when

Remembering Details (page 18)

1. Mrs. Fox said she'd rather have them die in peace than face the farmers' guns. 2. He thought his family would be too tired and weak to dig. 3. Mrs. Fox said she was too weak to be of any help. 4. He didn't want the Small Foxes to be too disappointed if they failed to reach his destination. 5. Down in the tunnel, they couldn't tell the difference between day and night. 6. The foxes dug their tunnel to Boggis's Chicken House Number One. 7. He didn't want anyone to know they had been there.

Discovering Meaning Through Context (page 19)

1. run; 2. hurting; 3. wonderful; 4. dim; 5. look; 6. slant; 7. opening; 8. scream; 9. filled; 10. make

Using Cloze Reading (page 21)

1. tunnel; 2. three; 3. bursting; 4. Mummy; 5. weaker; 6. dreaming; 7. House; 8. food; 9. strength; 10. feast; 11. fantastic

Matching Synonyms (page 22)

1. dug; 2. part; 3. left; 4. closest; 5. angrily; 6. fat; 7. all; 8. promise; 9. ran; 10. tell

Matching Antonyms (page 23)

1. noise; 2. borrowing; 3. above; 4. dull; 5. tough; 6. bored; 7. worst; 8. untrained; 9. tasteless; 10. hate

STUDY SKILLS

Determining Alphabetical Order (page 24)

A. 3; 4; 5; 1; 2
B. 1; 4; 3; 5; 2
C. 4; 3; 5; 1; 2
D. 1; 5; 3; 4; 2
E. 4; 3; 2; 5; 1

Choosing Correct Meanings (page 25)

1. mind; 2. turn; 3. sharp; 4. beat; 5. sip; 6. head; 7. foot; 8. close; 9. mind; 10. sip; 11. foot; 12. beat; 13. head; 14. close; 15. turn

Using Guide Words (page 27)

act—fin	final—march	mare—tongue
1. brick	1. glass	1. morning
2. cellar	2. gloom	2. noticed
3. crept	3. hundreds	3. poison
4. face	4. jar	4. second
5. fellow	5. Mabel	5. shelf

CREATIVE SKILLS

Writing a Journal Sample (page 28)
Responses will vary.

Creating a Picture (page 29)
Responses will vary.

Recalling a Character (page 30)
Responses will vary.

Writing a Book Recommendation (page 31)
Responses will vary.

Explaining Feelings (page 32)
Responses will vary.